“Whether you're a teacher or a parent, ‘Kenny Lives with Erica and M
way to introduce kids to different families, help tackle prejudice and
something to celebrate.”

– Tim Ramsey,

“We know that teachers are always looking for new, exciting ways to explore diversity, equality and inclusion. This book is the perfect way to start these vital conversations in the classroom.”

– Jac Bastian, Head of Education, Diversity Role Models

“It's time to ensure that every child grows up understanding and embracing diversity, equality and respect. This terrific story is not only an essential resource for combating LGBT+ related bullying, but it will inspire the next generation of young people and human rights campaigners.”

– Peter Tatchell, Director, Peter Tatchell Foundation

“Olly's books and resources play a crucial role in the quest for a united society. His work will help to shape the hearts and minds, not just of children, but of parents too.”

– Phyll Opoku-Gyimah, Executive Director and Co-Founder, UK Black Pride

“Olly Pike's work is always an inspiration to our younger generation and ‘Kenny Lives with Erica and Martina’ is another example of his wonderful talent to connect with our younger children and share with them themes of equality, compassion and kindness.”

– Sallyann Keizer, BAFTA award-winning Children's Media Producer

“A fantastic little read! A very thoughtful narrative covering the LGBT+ topic in a way which is very current, and much needed. Thank you Olly for tackling equality, diversity and inclusivity in a way which is easy to understand and very accessible for children.”

– Khakan Qureshi, Founder, Finding A Voice

Our Mission

Our mission is to create a more accepting world for future generations, and part of this mission is to make sure there is a copy of 'Kenny Lives with Erica and Martina' in every UK primary school.

To help us achieve this, and more, please visit www.popnolly.com/donate.

Notes for Grown-Ups

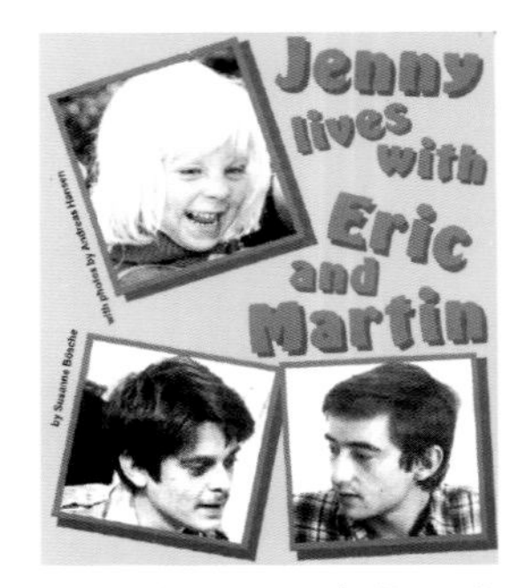

© 1981 Susanne Bösche/Fremad

The story you are about to read was inspired by another book called *Jenny Lives with Eric and Martin* (1981) (originally *Mette bor hos Morten og Erik*) by the Danish author Susanne Bösche. It was a black and white children's picture book about a little girl who lives with her father Martin and his partner Eric.

Bösche created the book to help educate children about family diversity. However, when Gay Men's Press published a UK edition of *Jenny Lives with Eric and Martin* in 1983 (a time in history when LGBT+ people were not treated fairly) much controversy accompanied it.

The book was unfairly vilified as 'homosexual propaganda', and the negativity surrounding it subsequently contributed to the passing of Section 28 - a law which forbade any local authority from intentionally promoting homosexuality, or publishing material with the intention of promoting homosexuality. It further forbade the teaching in any maintained school of the acceptability of homosexuality as a pretended family relationship.

It was a catastrophic setback for LGBT+ people.

The intention with my story is not to retell *Jenny Lives with Eric and Martin*, but rather draw inspiration from the unjust real-life events which followed its publication in the UK.

Section 28 was revoked in Scotland in 2000 and the rest of the UK in 2003. From September 2020 Relationship Education is mandatory in all UK primary schools.

I hope this book will educate children about diversity, equality and acceptance, and I hope it will inspire them to act whenever they see anyone else's human rights being compromised.

I'd like to thank Neal Cavalier-Smith (an LGBTQ+ activist and later owner of Gay Men's Press) for his support, inspiration and friendship.

Olly Pike
Director of Pop'n'Olly

To those who came before me,
To those I never met,
Thank you for the change you made,
I swear I won't forget.

First published in 2019
by Pop'n'Olly Ltd

www.popnolly.com

ISBN 978-0-9933407-7-2

Kenny Lives with Erica & Martina

Olly Pike

Pop'n'Olly

Kenny lived with his mum Erica and his mummy Martina.
They lived in a world where everything was grey.

The grass was grey, the sky was grey, the people were grey and nobody knew any different. But things were about to change…

“Wow!” said Kenny and his mums one morning as they stepped outside and saw something very different.

Another house, just like theirs, only this house wasn’t grey at all… It was colourful!

“Let’s see who lives there!” said Kenny to his mum and mummy.

They knocked on the door and two friendly faces answered. Faces which belonged to Jenny and Hasan.

Jenny and Hasan had just moved in: they were a couple and had a very colourful pet cat. The new neighbours chatted and quickly became friends.

Kenny really liked his new neighbours: they were nice, so he gave them one of his balloons.

Jenny and Hasan were grateful and in return gave Kenny a box of colourful paints.

Kenny and his family had made their new neighbours feel very welcome.

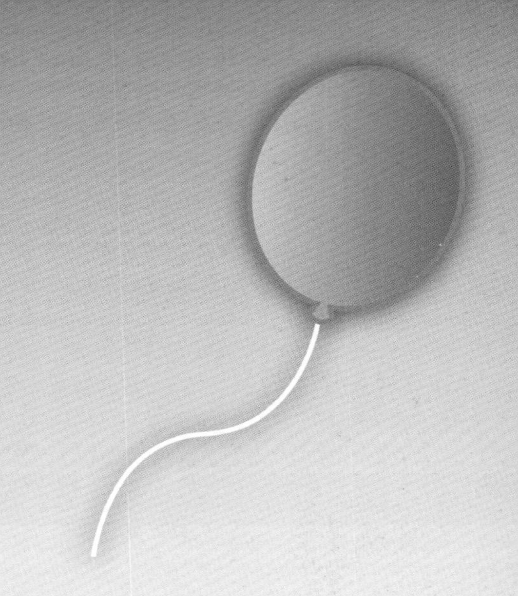

However, not everyone was so welcoming...

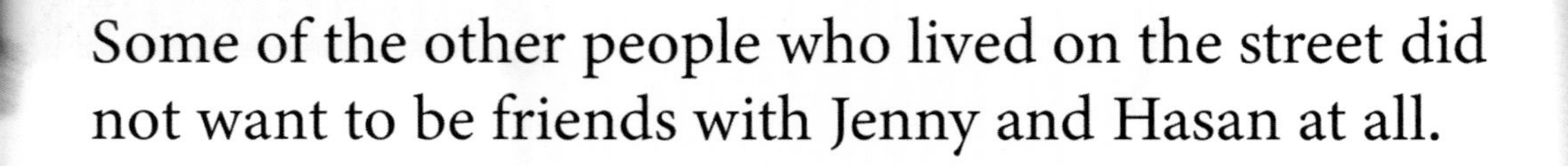

Some of the other people who lived on the street did not want to be friends with Jenny and Hasan at all.

In fact they wanted Jenny and Hasan to leave!

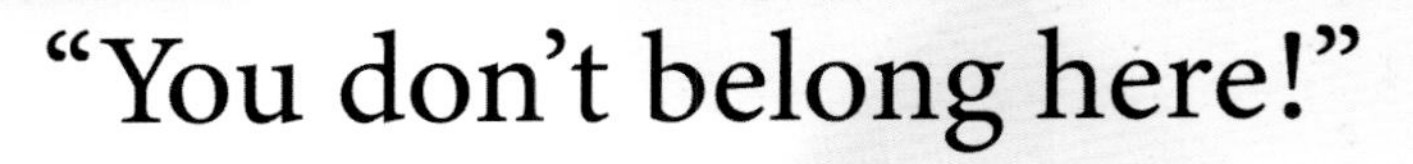

"You don't belong here!"

came one angry voice.

"We don't want you on our street!"

shouted another.

"You are too different!" said a third.

But Jenny and Hasan refused to leave.
"We belong here too!" they called back.

This made the people from the street even angrier...

“No, you can’t stay.”

“You’ll change everything.”

“You are different and frightening!”

Suddenly, before Kenny or his mums could do anything, Jenny and Hasan were rudely pushed inside their own home.

"We don't like different."

"We don't like change."

"And we don't want you here."

The people from the street were so angry that they decided to build a big, grey wall all the way around Jenny and Hasan's house.

They were going to pretend that Jenny and Hasan didn't exist by blocking them and their house completely out of sight.

Kenny was furious. “That’s not fair!” he shouted as he ran towards the newly finished wall.

Kenny tried to push it down, but it was too strong. He tried to climb it, but it was too high.

Kenny thought... and thought...

It was clear that Kenny could not change the wall.

“Maybe you could try and change the people on our street’s minds?” said one of Kenny’s mums.

“Yes, maybe they just need someone to help them understand that being different is not something to be scared of?” said the other.

Then Kenny remembered the paints that Jenny and Hasan had given him! Kenny started to paint immediately. The colours were beautiful.

Kenny painted his shoes and his kite and his bike. He painted his balloons and his football and his homework. He painted his clothes and he even painted his socks.

"Wow, that looks fantastic!" said Kenny's friends.

"Can you paint our stuff?"

"Of course..." said Kenny. "Aren't colours wonderful?"

Kenny's friends all agreed and he started to paint their belongings too.

Soon every child on Kenny's street was riding a colourful bike, or playing with colourful toys or wearing colourful clothes.

The children thought they looked wonderful!
But, once again, some of the adults just didn't understand...

“What is the meaning of this? You all look so different?!
Are you against us?”

Kenny bravely spoke up. “We’re not against you,” he said.

“We love our grey world, but don’t you see that the world isn’t grey for everyone? We can’t just pretend that differences don’t exist. Instead we should celebrate them!”

And with that Kenny and his friends splashed all of the different colours that they had at the big, grey wall...

...And it looked spectacular!

The adults on the street were stunned:
they had never seen something so beautiful.

“Wow. That does look...lovely... and interesting... and exciting... and almost... familiar, like it’s always belonged.”

“Yes, and look, it makes the grey look better too.”

“Maybe colours are ok?”

“No, colours are more than ok...” cried Kenny. “They are awesome!”

The whole street cheered at Kenny’s words, then everyone rushed towards the now very colourful wall and began pulling it down.

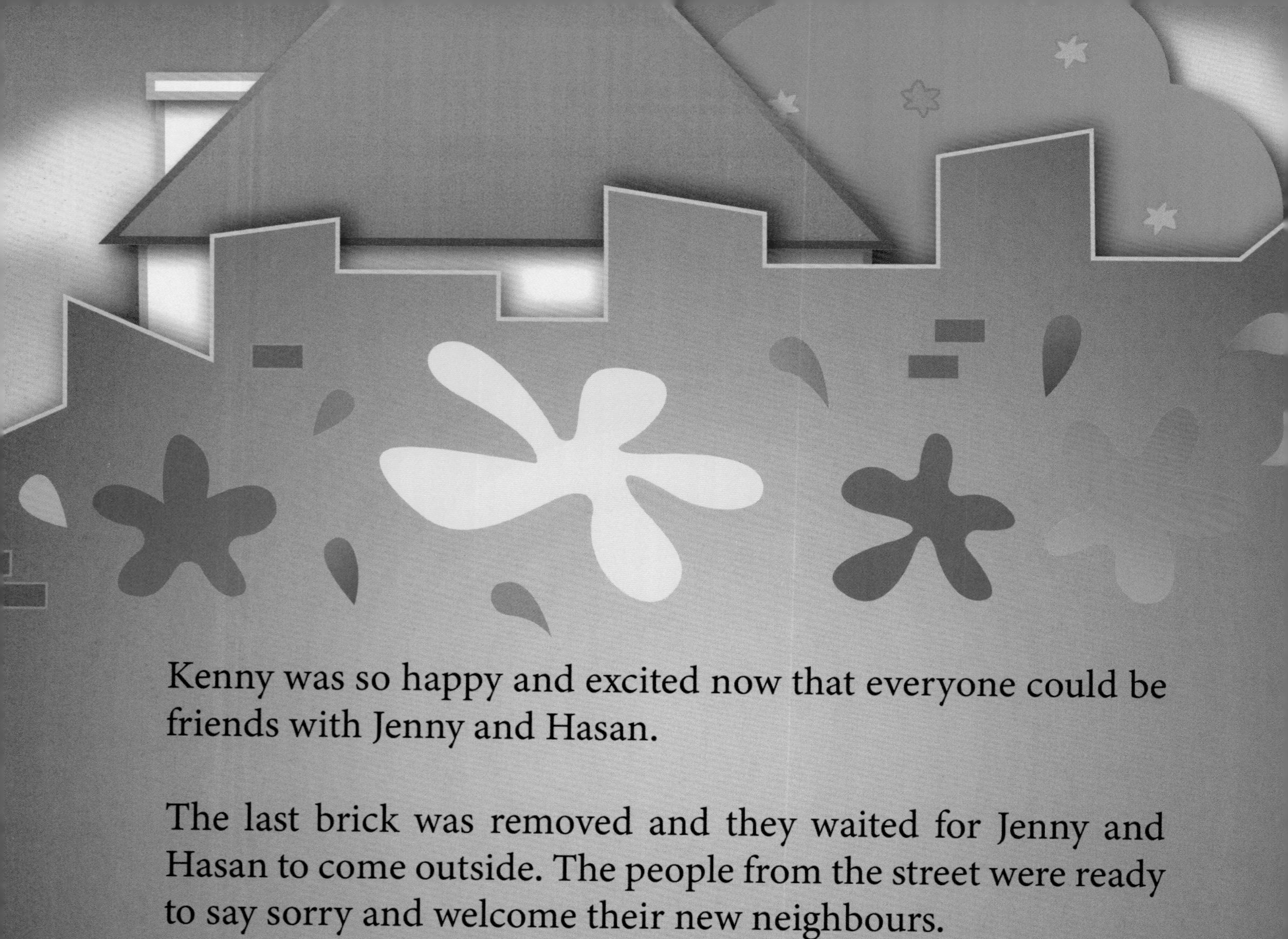

Kenny was so happy and excited now that everyone could be friends with Jenny and Hasan.

The last brick was removed and they waited for Jenny and Hasan to come outside. The people from the street were ready to say sorry and welcome their new neighbours.

They waited... and waited... But Kenny could wait no more. He ran up to the door...

“Oh, it’s unlocked.” Kenny crept in... “Hello?” he called.

Jenny and Hasan were gone. It was too late. Kenny began to cry.

“I know you are sad,” said Kenny’s mum. “And we are too, but look at the street, Kenny, look at all the colours. You helped change everyone’s mind. You helped to make the world a more colourful place. Jenny and Hasan would be very grateful.”

Kenny wiped away his tears, and thanked his mums.

“I know what we should do,” sniffed Kenny. “We should build the wall again.”

And so they did, but this time it was at the top of the street, and this time, it was less of a wall and more of a sign, because on it Kenny had added...

Everyone
is
Welcome

And Kenny hoped that wherever Jenny and Hasan were...

...They just might see it.

Lesson Ideas and Discussion Questions for Parents and Teachers

by Olly Pike and Mel Lane

Key Stage 1

The grey people are scared of anyone who is different from them. What could you say to help them not be scared of difference?
How do you think Jenny and Hasan felt when they saw the wall around their house?
Would you want to live on the grey street or the colourful street? Why?
What is the most important message in the story?
What things make people in your school the same and what things make people different?
Is it OK to be different?
How do we show that we treat people fairly in our school?

Key Stage 2

What does Kenny mean by *the world isn't grey for everyone*? Is this idea true for our world?
What was it that changed everyone's minds? (Hint - It wasn't the paint.)
What words would you use to describe Kenny? Do any of the words apply to you?
If Kenny didn't have a box of paints what else could he have done to change people's minds?
What does the word 'equality' mean?
What does the law in your country say about treating people equally?
If a wall was built around your school or home to keep you separate, how would you feel?

Activity for KS1 and KS2

Think about your school. Is it clear that everyone is welcome? What pictures or words would you put on a sign to make it clear? Could you make a sign to show that everyone is welcome? Where is the best place to display your sign so as many people as possible see it?

Additional Resource

An animated version of this story is availble to watch at:
popnolly.com/kennylivesvideo

Further Exploration for Older Children

by Olly Pike

Refer back to the **Notes for Grown-Ups** page and explain how this book was inspired by another book called *Jenny Lives with Eric and Martin*. Share a few pieces of information such as: the UK publishing date, what the story was about and perhaps where it originated from.

Then explore the following questions:

Why do you think the book *Jenny Lives with Eric and Martin* caused such a fuss at the time it was first published?

Can you think of any other times in history when books have been banned or when certain groups of people have been treated unfairly?

In this book the people from the street build a wall to keep Jenny and Hasan separate. Can you think of any other times when people have been separated or segregated?

What do you think it is that makes some people want to treat others unfairly?

Can you think of any famous leaders, politicians, activists, artists, or celebrities who have demonstrated and inspired ideas of equality and acceptance?

What does the word 'ally' mean? Who is an ally in this book?

One thought from this book is that sometimes it can take time for change to happen... However, time is not something we always have. What can you do today to make someone else feel welcome/be an ally?

popnolly.com

'Creating a more accepting world for future generations'

Help us to get a copy of this book into every UK primary school, and beyond, by visiting popnolly.com/donate.

Pop'n'Olly is an LGBTQIA+ and Equality educational resource used by children, parents, carers, and teachers. Our videos and books are being used in UK primary schools, and beyond, to teach about equality and diversity and ultimately combat homo-, bi- and transphobia.

Created by author/illustrator and YouTuber Olly Pike, Pop'n'Olly aims to 'usualise' different types of people, particularly those who are LGBTQIA+.

Our channel can be found at youtube.com/popnolly where we regularly produce fun and factual animations, stories and episodes.

For more information about our work please visit www.popnolly.com or contact us at info@popnolly.com.

Twitter @PopnOlly
Instagram @PopnOllyUK
Facebook Pop'n'Olly

Pop'n'Olly Books

Available from www.popnolly.com/shop or any good bookshop.

Goldilocks & the Five Bear Families
Family diversity for younger readers
ISBN 978 0 9933407 6 5

Jamie
A transgender Cinderella story
ISBN 978 0 9933407 3 4

The Prince and the Frog
An inclusive story about healthy relationships
ISBN 978 1 78592 382 1

Princess Penny & the Pea
An inclusive story about treating people how they wish to be treated
ISBN 978 0 9933407 5 8

Prince Henry
An equality fairytale romance
ISBN 978 0 9933407 4 1

Thank You

Once again I'd like to thank Neal Cavalier-Smith without whom this book would not have been possible.

I'd like to thank all those who follow and champion my work. Your excitement encourages and inspires me every day.

Also a special thank you to the following people who, if you look carefully, you might spot amongst the angry mob in this book! In real life they are not angry at all: in fact they are lovely, kind and generous, and they have helped me to continue my mission of creating LGBT+ and equality content for children. - Olly